Friendly Fred

Susannah McFarlane   Lachlan Creagh

A Scholastic Australia Book

This is Fred, with a few of his friends—
Freya, Fergus, Felix and Flora.

Fred is one of the friendliest fairy penguins you will find.

He has friends of all different feathers,
fins and fur. He fancies all kinds of fun!

Fred throws frisbees with flying foxes.

Fred goes fishing (even when it is freezing) with his fellow fairy penguins.

Fred picks flowers (his favourites
are frangipanis and freesias)

before playing the fiddle with
the frill-necked lizards.

Then one day, one Friday, in fact,
Fred couldn't find any of his friends.

Freaky!

Fred felt flabbergasted and flummoxed.

Fred was trying not to get in a flap

but was, frankly, feeling a little frazzled.

Fortunately, four finches
flew past with a big sign
flapping. The sign read,
'Follow us Fred, and fast!'

So Fred followed the finches
up the freeway for forty
kilometres in his four-wheel
drive and finally found . . .

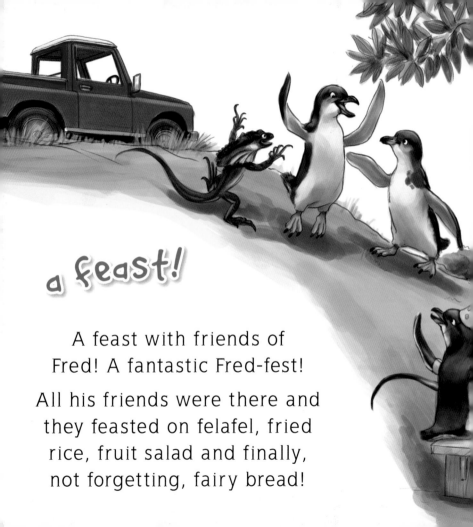

a feast!

A feast with friends of Fred! A fantastic Fred-fest!

All his friends were there and they feasted on felafel, fried rice, fruit salad and finally, not forgetting, fairy bread!

Then they all played a ferocious game
of footy—what fun!

Fair dinkum, what a fabulous Friday!

Good on you Fred (and Freya,
Fergus, Felix and Flora).

What about you?
Are you friendly too?